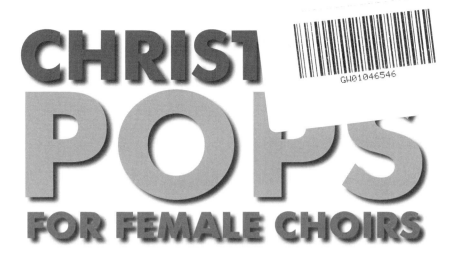

CHRIST POPS FOR FEMALE CHOIRS

GW01046546

Published by

Novello Publishing Limited
part of The Music Sales Group
14-15 Berners Street, London W1T 3LJ, UK.

Exclusive Distributors:

Music Sales Limited
Distribution Centre, Newmarket Road,
Bury St Edmunds, Suffolk IP33 3YB, UK.

Music Sales Pty Limited
Units 3-4, 17 Willfox Street, Condell Park
NSW 2200, Australia.

Order No. NOV163977
ISBN 978-1-78305-299-8

This book © Copyright 2013 Novello & Company Limited.

Edited by Ruth Power.
Music processed by Paul Ewers Music Design & Camden Music.

Printed in the EU.

Novello
part of The Music Sales Group
London / New York / Paris / Sydney / Copenhagen / Berlin / Madrid / Hong Kong / Tokyo

ALL I WANT FOR CHRISTMAS IS YOU

WORDS & MUSIC BY MARIAH CAREY & WALTER AFANASIEFF
Arranged by Christopher Hussey

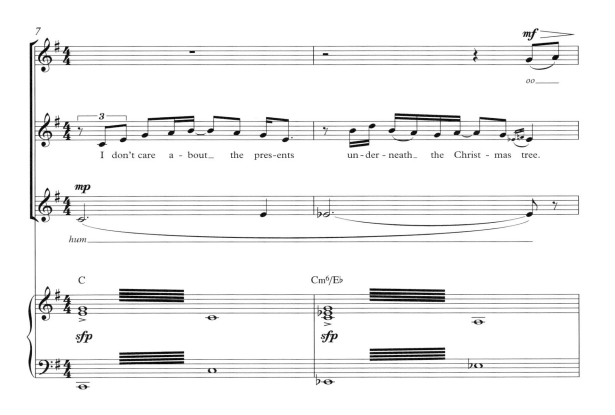

I don't care a-bout the pres-ents un-der-neath the Christ-mas tree.

hum

mm oo - mm oh

I just want you for my own, more than you could ev - er know.

mm oo - mm oh

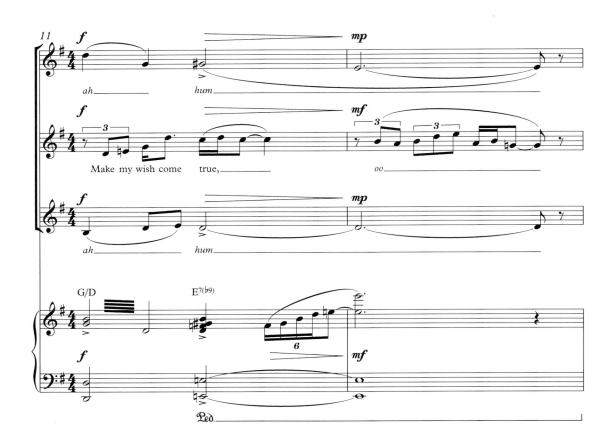

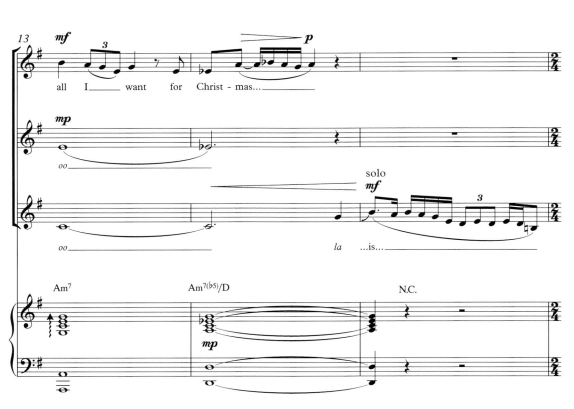

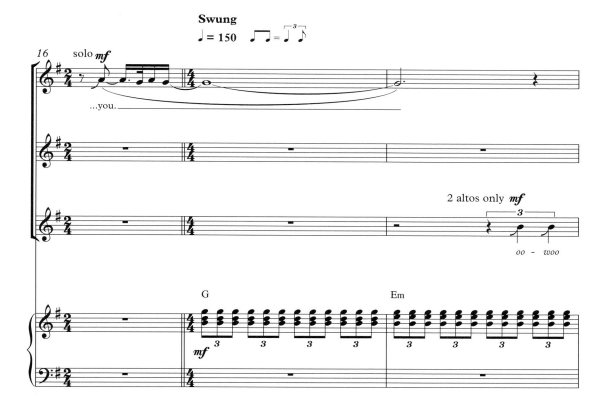

— for Christ - mas,— there is just one thing— I need.— And I....
— this Christ - mas,— I won't e - ven wish— for snow.—

tutti

Don't care a - bout— the pres - ents
I'm just gon - na keep— on wait - ing

un - der - neath_ the Christ - mas tree.__
un - der - neath_ the mis - tle - toe.__

I don't need_ to hang_
I won't make_ a list_

mm____

Cm6/Eb   G

__ my stock - ing... }
__ and send__ it... }

oo_____

__ there up - on__ the fire - place._____ }
to the North_ Pole for_____ Saint Nick._____ }

San - ta Claus won't make me hap - py with a toy on Ch - rist -
I won't ev - en stay a - wake to hear those mag - ic rein -

oo

I.

C   Cm⁶/E♭

- mas Day. I just want you for my own,
- deer click. I just want you here to - night,

I just want you for my own,
I just want you here to - night,

oo

G   B⁷aug

9

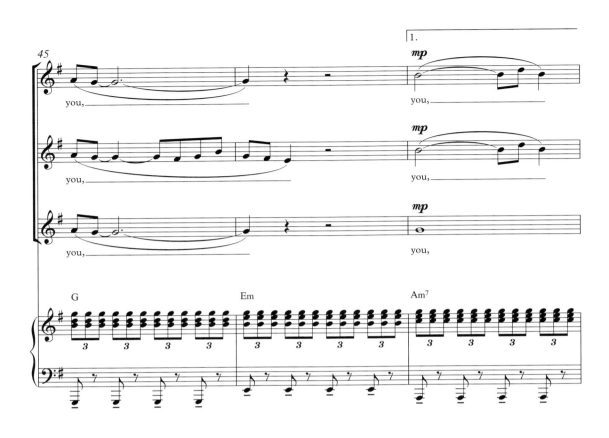

whoa All the lights are shin - ing so bright - ly ev - 'ry - where,

oo

oo

B⁷ Em

and the sound of chil - dren's

oo

oo

B⁷

11

for Christ - mas, this is all___ I'm ask - ing for.___

for Christ - mas, this is all___ I'm ask - ing for.___

And I just want to see___ my ba - by stand - ing right___ out - side___

I,___

15

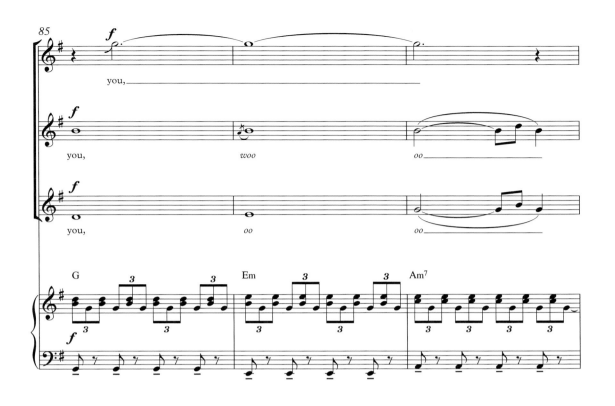

FAIRYTALE OF NEW YORK

WORDS & MUSIC BY SHANE MACGOWAN & JEM FINER

Arranged by Christopher Hussey

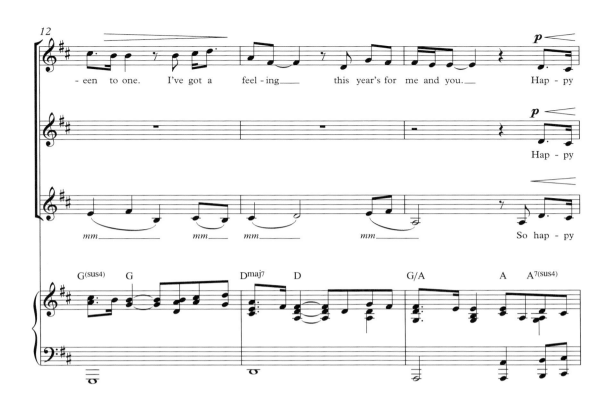

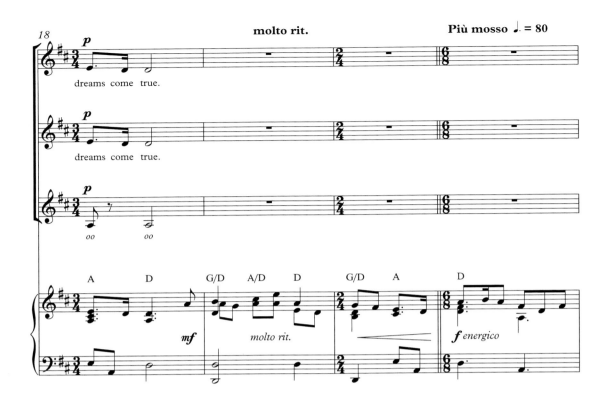

riv-ers of gold; but the wind goes right through you, it's no place for the old.__ When you

riv-ers of gold; but the wind goes right through you, it's no place for the old.__ When you

first took my hand on a cold__ Christ-mas Eve, you prom - ised me Broad-way was

first took my hand on a cold__ Christ-mas Eve, you prom - ised me Broad-way was

23

oo_____ oo oo_____ The

oo_____ oo oo_____ The

drunks they were sing-ing. We kissed on the cor - ner, then danced through the night._ The

boys of the N. Y. P. D. choir___ were sing-ing___ 'Gal - way Bay'. And the

boys of the N. Y. P. D. choir___ were sing-ing___ 'Gal - way Bay'. And the

boys of the N. Y. P. D. choir___ were sing-ing___ 'Gal - way Bay'. And the

bells were ring-ing out for Christ-mas Day.____

bells were ring-ing out for Christ-mas Day.____

bells were ring-ing out for Christ-mas Day.____

Bay'. And the bells were ring-ing out for Christ-mas Day.____

Bay'. And the bells were ring-ing out for Christ-mas Day.____

Bay'. And the bells were ring-ing out for Christ-mas Day.____

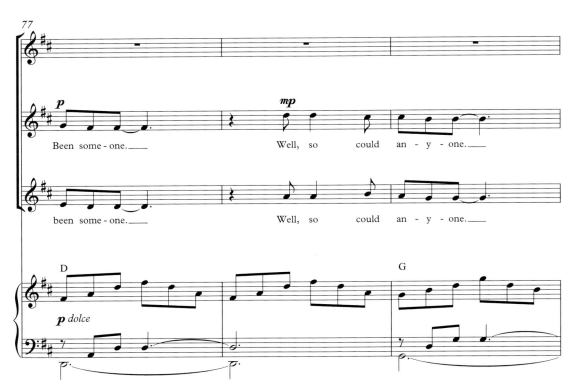

You took my dreams from me when I first found_ you._

You took my dreams from me when I first found_ you._

I put them with my own._

With me, babe._ I put them with my own._

I kept them with me, babe._ oo la_____

LITTLE SAINT NICK

WORDS & MUSIC BY BRIAN WILSON & MIKE LOVE
Arranged by Peter Foggitt

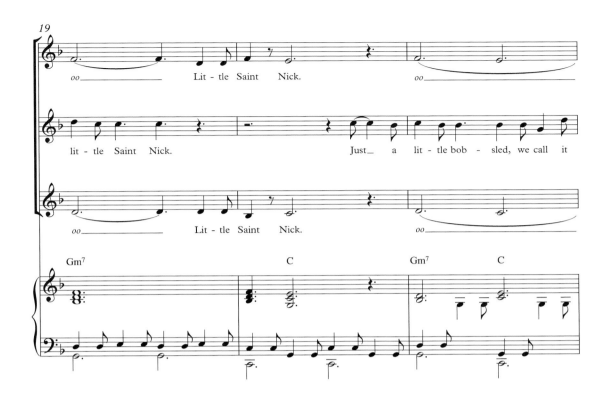

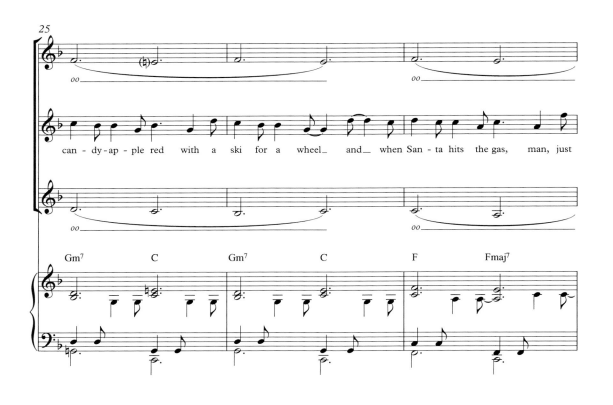

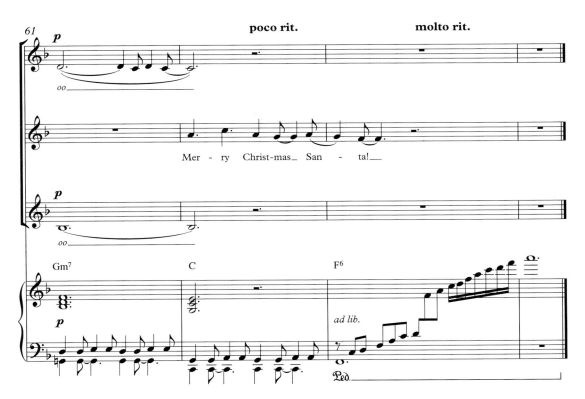

WONDERFUL CHRISTMASTIME

WORDS & MUSIC BY PAUL MCCARTNEY
Arranged by Christopher Hussey & Jeremy Birchall

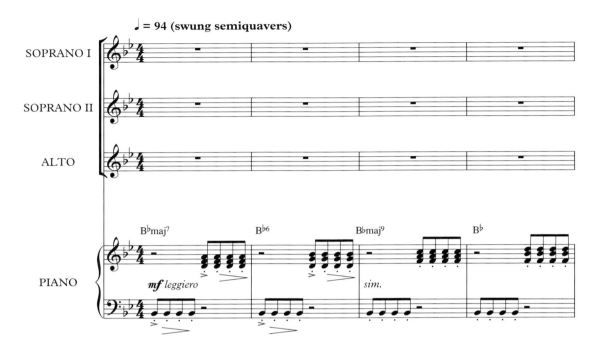

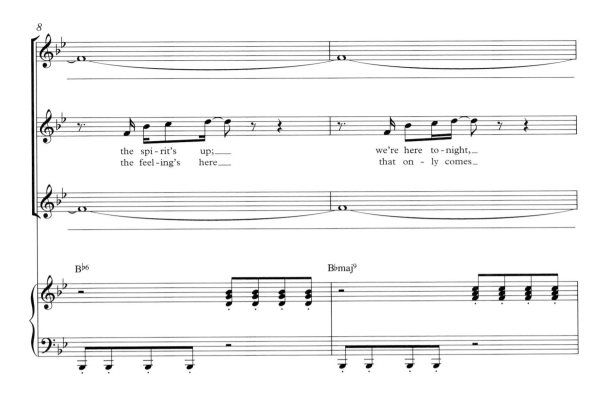

the spi-rit's up;___ we're here to-night,___
the feel-ing's here___ that on - ly comes___

B♭6 B♭maj9

___ Sim - ply hav - ing a won-der-ful Christ-mas-time.

and that's e - nough.___ } Sim - ply hav - ing a won-der-ful Christ-mas-time.
this time of year.___ }

___ Sim - ply hav - ing a won-der-ful Christ-mas-time.

B♭ Cm7 F9 Dm7 Gm9 E♭maj7 A♭9 B♭

mf

Sim - ply hav - ing a won - der - ful Christ-mas - time.

Sim - ply hav - ing... oo

Sim - ply hav - ing a won - der - ful Christ-mas - time.

The choir of chil - dren sing their song. doo

The choir of chil - dren sing their song. doo doo

Of chil - dren sing their song.

49

They prac - tised

The choir of chil - dren.

Of chil - dren sing their song. _____

Cm/B♭   F   B♭6

mf

all year long.   ding

ding dong ding dong ding dong ding

_____ oo   ding dong ding dong ding dong ding

Cm⁷/B♭   F   B♭   E♭/B♭ B♭6   E♭/B♭   B♭

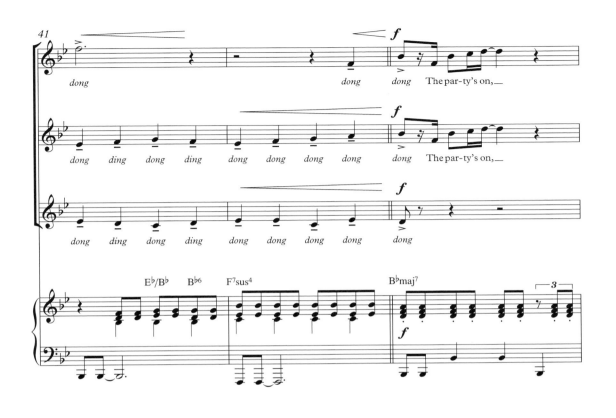

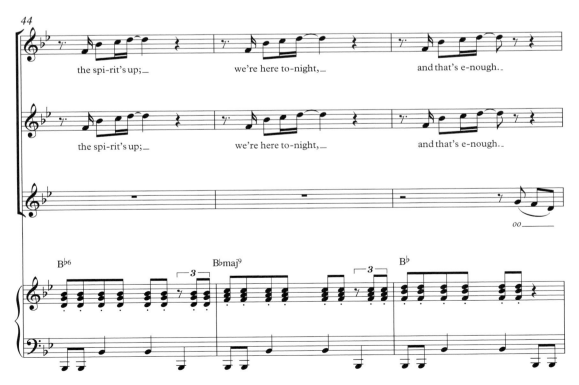

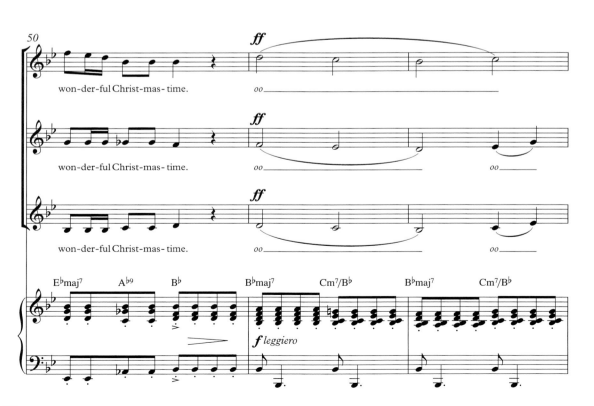

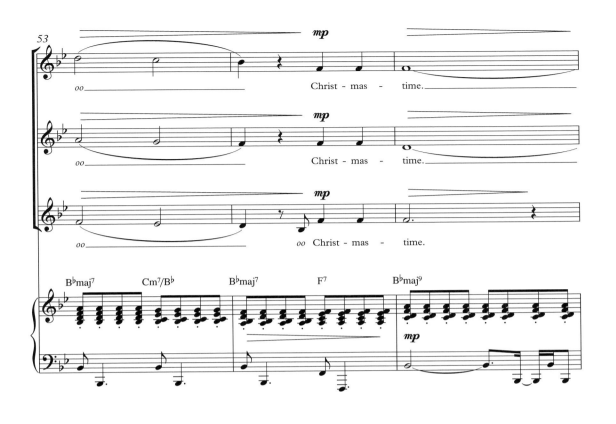

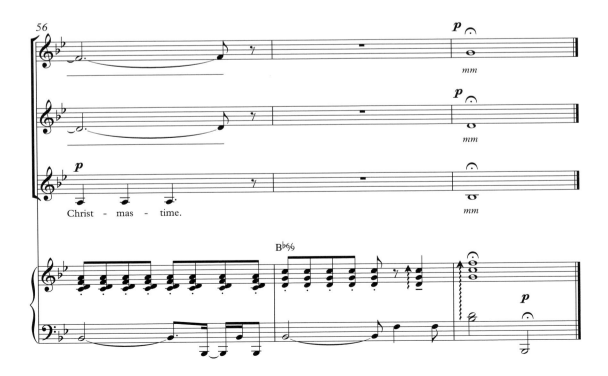

SANTA BABY

WORDS & MUSIC BY JOAN JAVITS, PHIL SPRINGER & TONY SPRINGER
Arranged by Jonathan Wikeley

Santa baby, so hur-ry down the chim-ney to-night.

Eb Eb/G Fm Bb Eb Bb

ooh

ooh

Santa baby, a fif-ty four con-ver-ti-ble too, light blue.

Eb Eb/G Fm Bb G Cm

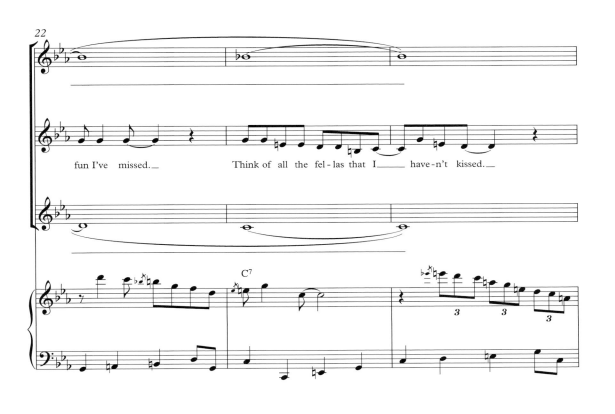

fun I've missed.___ Think of all the fel-las that I___ have-n't kissed.___

C7

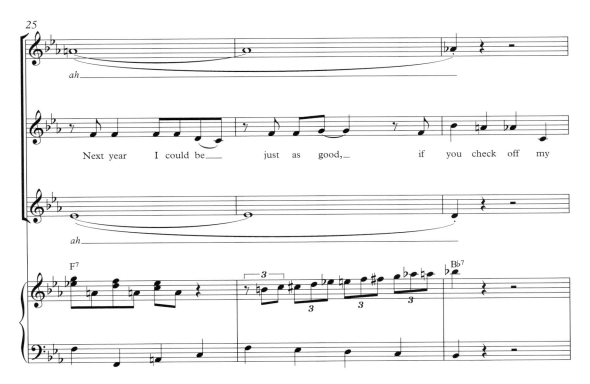

ah___ Next year I could be___ just as good,___ if you check off my

ah___

F7

B♭7

59

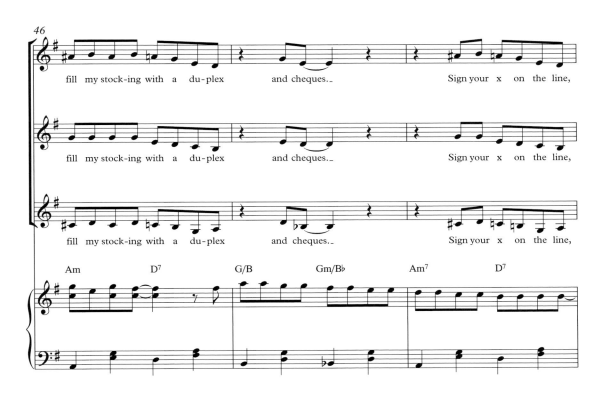

61

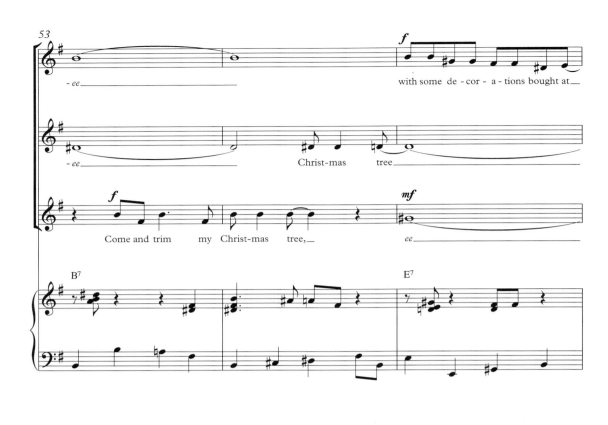

123456789